Mary Katherine Kasper
The tiny mustard-seed of love

Editor:
ECHO BUCHVERLAG
Fichtenweg 8
7607 Neuried

Editorial Staff:
Central Pastoral Team
of the Poor Handmaids of
Jesus Christ.

Script:
Raymond Piela

Drawer:
Pierre Huffner

D1224440

ISBN 3-927095-00-1
1989

Printed in France by Girold

KATHERINE KASPER WAS BORN ON MAY 26, 1820 IN DERNBACH, A SMALL VILLAGE NOT FAR FROM MONTABAUR IN WEST GERMANY.
HER PARENTS WERE SIMPLE FARMERS AND LIVED WITH THE BARE NECESSITIES.
THOSE WERE HARD TIMES.

KATHERINE'S BIRTHPLACE

THE PEOPLE LIVED ON WHAT THE LAND PRODUCED AND THEIR ANIMALS PROVIDED.

FROM HER PARENTS KATHERINE RECEIVED A SIMPLE CHRISTIAN UPBRINGING.

Come, Lord Jesus, be our guest, bless these gifts you have given us.

Amen!

HER FATHER AND MOTHER HAD THE DIFFICULT TASK OF BRINGING UP EIGHT CHILDREN, SO KATHERINE GREW UP IN POVERTY AND WITH LITTLE INDIVIDUAL ATTENTION.

KATHERINE STARTED SCHOOL ON MAY 8, 1826.

BECAUSE SHE WAS OFTEN SICK AS A CHILD, SHE DID NOT ATTEND SCHOOL REGULARLY.

BUT WHEN SHE WAS ABLE TO GO TO SCHOOL, SHE LEARNED SO QUICKLY AND WORKED SO DILIGENTLY THAT HER TEACHER ONCE SAID:

ON HER OWN, BECAUSE OF HER INNATE ABILITY, SHE SPENT MOST OF HER TIME ON RELIGION AND READING.

Katherine, you would be one of my best students if you attended more regularly.

EVERYTHING RELIGIOUS CAME EASILY TO HER AND SHE COULD REPEAT EVERY WORD FAITHFULLY. AFTER CHURCH ON SUNDAYS, STANDING ON A CHAIR, SHE WOULD REPEAT PARTS OF THE SERMON TO HER PARENTS.

SHE WAS KIND TO OTHERS, EVEN TO HER CLASSMATES IN SCHOOL.

KATHERINE LOVED IT IN THE SUMMER, WHEN HER FATHER SHOOK THE BIG PEAR TREE.

SHE WAS ALLOWED TO KEEP ALL THE PEARS SHE COULD PICK UP.

Tell me, child, what are you going to do with all those pears?

Give them to the other children!

IN LATER YEARS SHE CONFIDED: "IT WAS ALWAYS IMPORTANT TO ME TO BE KIND TO OTHERS."

WE DON'T KNOW TOO MANY OF KATHERINE'S ACTUAL WORDS AS A CHILD, BUT WE KNOW THAT SOMETIMES SHE WAS WISE BEYOND HER YEARS. ONCE, SHE STARTLED HER MOTHER BY SAYING...

Oh, mother, if only we were really, really poor, I would be so happy!

What are you talking about? Poorer than we are?

But child, we are very poor! One would think you were crazy to have such a wish!

8

"WHEN I FINISHED SCHOOL," SHE LATER SAID, "AND AFTER MY FIRST COMMUNION, I WANTED TO GET CLOSER TO GOD, BUT I DIDN'T KNOW HOW TO GO ABOUT IT."

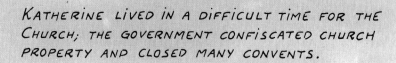

KATHERINE LIVED IN A DIFFICULT TIME FOR THE CHURCH; THE GOVERNMENT CONFISCATED CHURCH PROPERTY AND CLOSED MANY CONVENTS.

THROUGHOUT KATHERINE'S NEIGHBORHOOD, EMPTY CONVENTS COULD BE FOUND. THESE UNUSED BUILDINGS SEEMED TO POINT TO THE END OF RELIGIOUS LIFE.

Katherine's family lived, as already indicated, in poor circumstances. After leaving school she had to work hard, wherever her parents needed her. Katherine helped out without complaining.

The "Heilborn Shrine" of Dernbach played a very important role in Katherine's life. Even as a young girl she used to take the village children there and talk to them about God.

More and more she felt a great desire for solitude, silence and prayer. Therefore, she liked to work alone in the fields.

"Surrounded by the peace and quiet of nature," she later told another sister, "I felt as free as a bird chirping in the branches of the trees overhead. I had to sing the praise of the Creator like that bird. There I experienced God's presence within me."

SHE NEEDED THE GUIDANCE OF THE HOLY SPIRIT BECAUSE DIFFICULT YEARS LAY AHEAD.

ON JANUARY 26, 1842, HER FATHER DIED AT THE AGE OF 68.

Lord, have mercy on his soul!

HER FAMILY'S HOME HAD TO BE AUCTIONED.

Oh, dear God, make me rich in spiritual gifts.

NOW AN EVEN GREATER EFFORT WAS NEEDED TO EARN ENOUGH MONEY FOR HER MOTHER AND KATHERINE. SO KATHERINE TOOK ON EVERY KIND OF WORK OFFERED HER.

Katherine, you are breaking stones! And under this scorching sun? That's no work for a young girl!

SUDDENLY HER FACE LIT UP, HER EYES SHONE AS SHE PICTURED A VAST NUMBER OF SISTERS ALL DRESSED IN THE EXACT RELIGIOUS HABIT LATER WORN BY THE POOR HANDMAIDS OF JESUS CHRIST.

SHE DID NOT UNDERSTAND THE MEANING OF THIS EXTRAORDINARY VISION. SO TO PUT HER MIND AT REST, SHE APPROACHED THE DEAN OF MONTABAUR, FATHER HEIMANN FOR ADVICE.

I suppose you've been wasting your life up to now and have decided it's time to get your conscience cleared.

AFTER THEIR CONVERSATION AND AFTER HEARING KATHERINE'S CONFESSION, DEAN HEIMANN ALTERED HIS OPINION OF KATHERINE. HE ALLOWED HER TO RECEIVE HOLY COMMUNION SEVERAL TIMES A WEEK WHICH WAS UNUSUAL IN THOSE DAYS.

AFTER THIS SHE OFTEN TRAVELED TO LIMBURG TO VISIT THE BISHOP TO TALK WITH HIM ABOUT HER PLANS TO BUILD A LITTLE HOUSE.

SHE DID NOT GIVE UP, HOWEVER, BUT CONTINUED TO VISIT BISHOP BLUM. AFTER A FEW MEETINGS WITH KATHERINE, HE WAS CONVINCED THAT SHE HAD A GENUINE CALL FROM GOD AND THAT ONLY GOOD COULD COME FROM IT.

SHE USED TO SPEND THE NIGHT IN LIMBURG; THE BISHOP ORDERED THAT HER BASKET BE FILLED WITH GROCERIES, AND SHE HERSELF BE SENT HOME WITHOUT SEEING HIM.

I want to help you!

Katherine is going to confession again!

She must have a lot on her conscience!

You are wrong! Katherine is a good Christian young woman.

THE VILLAGERS OF DERNBACH WITNESSED, NOT ONLY KATHERINE'S GOOD LIFE, BUT ALSO THE LOVING THINGS SHE DID.
ON SUNDAYS AND HOLIDAYS, SHE TOOK A LITTLE BASKET OF GIFTS AND VISITED THE OLD AND SICK PEOPLE OF THE VILLAGE. SHE TRIED TO HELP AND COMFORT THEM IN THEIR NEEDS.

GOD USED HER TO TOUCH THE HEARTS OF THE PEOPLE. IT WASN'T LONG BEFORE HEARTS OPENED TO RESPOND TO GOD'S CALL.

KATHERINE AND HER MOTHER RENTED A ROOM FROM THE MULLERS THEIR DAUGHTER ANNE MARIE WAS THE FIRST VILLAGER TO JOIN KATHERINE IN HER WORK.

If there are two of us, we can do much more to help the sick and those who are suffering.

SOON AFTERWARDS THE FOLLOWING YOUNG WOMEN JOINED THE GROUP: KATHERINE SCHOENBERGER, MARIA MAGDALENA RITZ, KATHARINE NEBGEN, KATHARINE MANNS, KATHARINE MARSCHANG. GRADUALLY THE GROUP TOOK ON THE CHARACTER OF A SOCIETY.

The aim of our society is to live loving Christian lives by example, teaching and prayer.

15

KATHERINE KASPER STROVE TO INSTILL INTO HER GROUP A GENEROUS AND DEDICATED SPIRIT THROUGH COMMUNITY PRAYER AND SPIRITUAL READING.

Don't worry who is for you or who is against you, but let your work and your goal be to remember that God is with you in everything.

THE SOCIETY INCREASED IN NUMBERS AND GRADUALLY DEVELOPED INTO THE FORM OF A RELIGIOUS COMMUNITY.
BUT HOW COULD THIS BECOME A REALITY.

SHE OFTEN HEARD AN INNER VOICE, SAYING TO HER:

Build a little house!

BUT, OF COURSE, SHE HAD NO MONEY. HER MOTHER SHOOK HER HEAD AND SIGHED:

What? You want to build a house? Without money? How are you going to do it?

Don't worry mother! I only want to do God's Will.

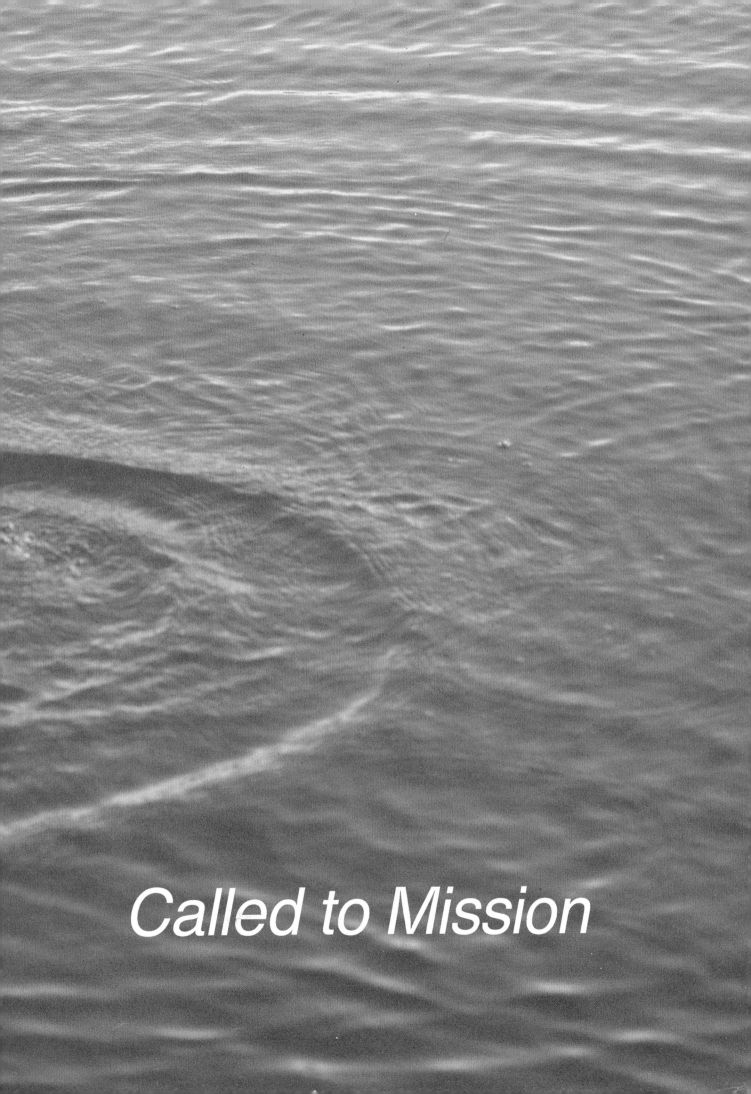

Called to Mission

The first eight Sisters to come to America in 1868 were (top - bottom), (left - right) -- Sisters Henrika, Rose, Bel
Hyacintha, Corona, Eudoxia, Fecunda and Matrona.

Mother Mary Katherine Kasper never dreamed she would be sending some of her sisters to far away America when she founded a religious community in the tiny German village of Dernbach. It was the farthest thing from her mind. All that mattered was that she serve God by tending to the needs of the poor in her community.

Born into a peasant family in 1820, Katherine Kasper, though of fragile health, worked in the fields, helped build roads with her neighbors, learned to weave and sew. Like all of her social class, her education was limited.

Even more limited was her religious education. What made this peasant girl different from others her age was her intense desire to further her knowledge of religion and help the poor and sick of Dernbach.

This she did, eventually drawing several other young women to her simple, caring work. Guided by the Spirit she built her "little house", a center from which the sick of her village were nursed and in which a home was provided for a widow and eight orphans.

Getting started as a congregation was not easy in Germany of the 1840's which was filled with political and religious uncertainties. Despite wagging tongues and suspicious clerics, Katherine Kasper and her four companions pronounced their vows August 15, 1851.

The congregation of Poor Handmaids of Jesus Christ grew rapidly. Only eight years after its founding, convents were established in six other German dioceses and in Holland.

In the aftermath of America's Civil War came a call from the Ft. Wayne diocese for help in ministering to German immigrants. Difficult as it was to send her sisters so far away, Mother Mary took the risk and sent eight sisters off to the strange country of the United States of America.

The eight sisters selected for the American mission were Sisters Eudoxia, Hyacintha, Matrona, Fecunda, Bella, Henrica, Corona, and Rose.

Mother Mary wrote concerning the departure on July 30, 1868, "With tears in my eyes I watched the vessel from the shore until I lost sight of it."

Mission Statement

Called in Baptism to proclaim by our lives and our works the presence of God in the world, we Poor Handmaids of Jesus Christ accept the invitation to live a vowed life in community.

We are inspired by Mary, the Mother of Jesus, and Blessed Katherine Kasper, our foundress, to

> *listen prayerfully*
> *live simply*
> *serve joyfully.*

Empowered by the same Spirit, we women religious commit ourselves to

- *respect and value each person we serve in our diverse ministries*

- *stand with the poor and powerless in the search for justice*

- *use our talents and resources in response to the emerging needs of Church and society*

- *share ministry and nurture leadership in our efforts to bring peace to the world.*

Resisting our fears, we dare to accept the challenges of the future. We go forward in hope and joy supported by the bond of community and the strength of prayer.

Poor Handmaids of Jesus Christ
American Province

... the presence of God in the world.

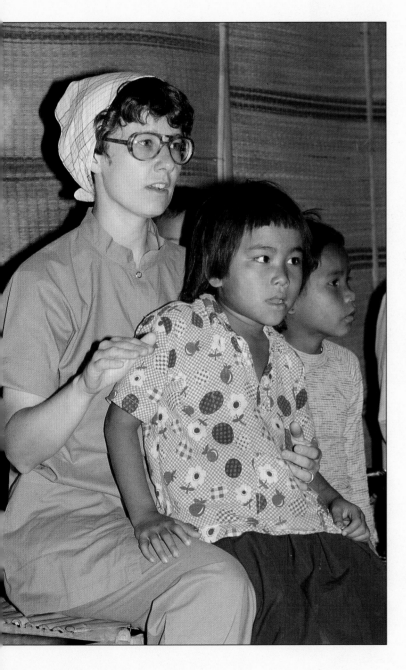

At times that witnessing calls for additional risk-taking. Such was the case as Poor Handmaids saw needs arise in Thailand and Cambodia. Like Mother Mary before them, they were drawn once again to orphans created by war.

Poor Handmaids of Jesus Christ accept the invitation to live a vowed life in community.

With the acceptance of the invitation comes support from the community, support in remaining single-minded, in listening to the spirit.

From community flows strength... strength to face the task each day brings, knowing others are praying for you and with you, listening to you, waiting for your return and shared story.

From community flows joy... joy in serving God reflected in hearts lifted in prayer, song and laughter.

Whether in family or as a single person, we form community by being present for each other, sharing joys and sorrows... listening. If we are fearful of relationships that ask for commitment, however, community dies.

Community is found in participating, welcoming and giving ourselves to church. In community, the Spirit is visible.

.. to use our talents and resources in response to the emerging needs of church and society.

On the other hand, if the need be to feed the poor, a sister works in a soup kitchen in the heart of Chicago's south side. Another operates a clinic for the poor in East St. Louis. Others open their convent to elderly women who have no home. Still others work with the handicapped, teach, tutor, and instruct adults working towards a high school equivalency diploma.

Their work is as diverse as needs are perceived. Besides serving as catechists in parishes, they take an active role in parish activities, visit the home of parishioners, meet with citizens in planning self-help programs and programs which reach out to the community.

... to share ministry and nurture leadership in our

Mary Katherine Kasper, foundress of the Poor Handmaids of Jesus Christ, sought to help those caught in a social structure which denied the poor and powerless educational and social rights.

Today's Poor Handmaids reach out for peace and justice as well.

As the existence of hospitals which serve the poor are threatened by unjust laws, Poor Handmaids assume the role of justice advocate.

In protest lines they stand to defend a neighbor's right to clean water, uncontaminated by a nearby toxic landfill. In the legislatures they ask for just laws for family farmers.

They open their homes to political exiles from Central America. These refugees are denied rights granted to those seeking asylum from other countries of the world.

efforts to bring peace to the world.

With their families, friends and co-workers, sisters share their ministry and encourage participation in their activities through the Associate Program. A sincere desire to belong to the PHJC community has led many women and men to enter the program.

Associates join Poor Handmaids in prayer and scripture study. They provide food, clothing and other needs through the Outreach Program in Cairo, Illinois where they help operate a store. In other cities they are similarly involved with caring for the elderly, poor and lonely.

The summer volunteer program in Appalachia offers another opportunity for Associate involvement. Many Associates find their own way to carry out PHJC ministries. One couple carries jugs of water to residents living near a toxic landfill. Out of her rural home, another offers clothing to the needy.

In such ways, Associates endeavor to live the PHJC Mission.

Called in Baptism to proclaim by our lives and our works the presence of God in the world.

Today, Poor Handmaids continue in the path set before them, reaching out to the needs of the times.

In asking themselves where best to serve the Church and its people, Poor Handmaids expand their ministries. Keeping in mind their own Godgiven gifts, they serve as pastoral ministers, directors of religious education both in parishes and at the diocesan level, as visiting nurses in the homes of AID's victims and see to the needs of the elderly.

.. to respect and value each person we serve in our diverse ministries.

The first Poor Handmaids of Jesus Christ arrived in Hessen Cassel, Indiana, on the back of a hay-rack. They were greeted by the German immigrant community on the Feast of St. Rose of Lima.

Of their home in America Sister Eulogia writes, "The attic could not be used because there was neither staircase nor ladder to get up there. We did not need the cellar because our supply of food was never very great, but it was always sufficient."

Even though their numbers were few, the First American Chronicle of Poor Handmaids in America recorded "we took charge of the elementary school, were assigned to nursing the sick in the neighborhood, the cleaning and decorating of the church, the washing of church linen as well as the playing of the organ."

The diverse ministry of the Poor Handmaids in America had begun.

... to stand with the poor and powerless in the search for justice.

Mindful of their foundress' dedication to the poor and powerless, the small band of American sisters responded with a quick "yes" to the request made in 1868 by Fr. Peter Fischer to administer an Orphan Home in Chicago.

The Civil War and diseases prevalent in that day had created many orphans. Sister Hyacinth became the first superior of the home, later known as Angel Guardian Orphanage.

On the heels of this move came the opening of St. Joseph Hospital in Ft. Wayne.

Poor Handmaid compassion for the sick and helpless came to a dramatic point in 1882 when the sisters agreed to direct the operation of the "pox house", an isolation hospital for victims of smallpox in Chicago.

We are inspired by Mary, the Mother of Jesus, and Blessed Katherine Kasper, our foundress to
listen prayerfully
live simply
serve joyfully.

Poor Handmaids of Jesus Christ respond to God's call humbly and with faith as Mary responded in her Magnificat.

In patterning their lives after Mary, the Mother of God, Poor Handmaids follow the example of their foundress Blessed Mary Katherine Kasper, a simple peasant woman who prayerfully listened to God's quiet call to serve his people. Her joy in serving her neighbors endeared her to everyone.

Each of us has a similar call. We hear it through prayerful listening. By serving joyfully we witness to the call and our intent to act upon it.

Resisting our fears, we dare to accept the challenges o
the future. We go forward in hope and joy.

Fear prevents us from accepting challenges. Arme
with faith and hope in God, Katherine Kasper con
quered her fears and constantly risked to accomplis
what she perceived as God's work.

Today Poor Handmaids of the American Provinc
take up the challenge of the future by declaring them
selves a *sanctuary community* - a community whic
opens its doors to political refugees of Centr:
America who are not granted the same privileges i
the United States as are those from other parts of th
world.

Again, seeing the growing spiritual and physical neec
of a poverty-stricken population south of the borde
Poor Handmaids of the American Province recent
chose to share their ministry with the people of Coat
zacoalcos, Mexico.

In baptism we are all called to be a hope for someon
to witness to good and expose evil. The challenge lie
before each of us. How we accept it makes all the di
ference.

Poor Handmaids of Jesus Christ

Dear Reader,

The Poor Handmaids of Jesus Christ invite you to join in their work... in their ministry.

How does one do that? Of course, the hoped-for response is "join the community" as a member or Associate. Accordingly, you are invited to come and see, to find out more about our lifestyle, to spend some time in our home and share your aspirations and dreams with us as we share them with you.

Would you be surprised to hear that in your present lifestyle you may be living the Poor Handmaid mission and witnessing to God's presence in the world? Let's explore that idea a bit further:

Do you, for example, call or visit a lonely or sick relative, friend, or neighbor once in awhile? Well then, you are participating in PHJC ministry.

Do you open a whole new world to children and adults by teaching them to read? So do the Poor Handmaids.

Do you ask your spouse, children, friends, the people with whom you work how their day went and listen to their response? You are witnessing to God's presence in the world for sure!

Do you greet the person next to you in the pew on Sunday... even if you don't know the individual personally? And do you sometimes ask that total stranger to join you for a cup of coffee after services or to accompany you to a church activity? You've got the idea!

Have you written a letter to your legislative representative or congress person about an unjust law or other justice issue? Being a voice standing for the poor and powerless is strong witnessing!

Do you regularly collect good used clothing and furniture for the needy or monetarily help missions to the extent you can afford? The Poor Handmaids and Associates do that, too.

... And the list could go on and on. What really matters, you see, is that you and I are windows through which others catch a glimpse of God's loving and caring presence in the world. Sounds lofty? Sounds scary!

But that is what we are when we live as Katherine Kasper. She did not leave the world. She joined it the only way she knew how. In so doing, through her Poor Handmaids, she opened countless windows to God's love and presence. We are asked to do no more. But we are asked to do.

In order to emphasize how each of their lives affect those around them, the Poor Handmaids of Jesus Christ of the American Province have chosen a rippling pool of water as their symbol. In explaining their choice, they state,

"A rippling pool of water captures the broad impact created by a small force. ... Each action makes a difference. ... We move with the flow of life to do our work from our Christ-centered belief in the impact of love on the world."

Convent Ancilla Domini
P.O. Box 1
Donaldson, IN 46413
(219) 936-9936

Photo Acknowledgements: 1. John A. Zierten
2. Northwest Indiana Catholic

KATHERINE HAD GREAT FAITH. SHE TRUSTED IMPLICITLY THAT GOD WOULD ASSIST HER IF SHE OBEYED THE VOICE WITHIN. IT WASN'T HER IDEA TO BUILD THE "LITTLE HOUSE." SHE ALWAYS THOUGHT "IF GOD WANTS THIS HE WILL SUPPLY THE MONEY."

May God's holy will be done as perfectly now at the beginning and until the end as my Lord and God wishes it. You alone, O God, shall be Lord and Master.

ON AUGUST 15TH, 1848, THE WORK WAS COMPLETED AND THEY COULD MOVE IN.

THE HOUSE WAS MADE OF SIMPLE WHITE-WASHED WALLS; THE ONLY FURNISHINGS CONSISTED OF A TABLE, A CHAIR, A BED, AND A SMALL STOVE.

It reminds me of Bethlehem or the little house at Nazareth.

The little house of Nazareth was our birthplace! All our houses must be modeled on Nazareth.

NOW, AT LAST, SHE HAD BUILT THE LITTLE HOUSE, A PLACE FOR PRAYER AND REFLECTION; A CENTER FOR SOCIAL CHARITABLE WORK. AS SOON AS SHE MOVED IN, SHE IMMEDIATELY TOOK IN A GIRL WHO WAS HANDICAPPED AND A WIDOW WITH ONE CHILD. KATHERINE CONTINUED TO WORK SO THAT SHE COULD PAY OFF THE REMAINDER OF THE DEBT ON THE "LITTLE HOUSE", AND HAVE ENOUGH ON WHICH TO LIVE.

In early summer of 1849 a new impetus was given to the little society. Bishop Peter Joseph Blum from Limburg, who was travelling from Montabaur to Wirges, made a detour to Dernbach, to visit Katherine's "Little House". He blessed it and expressed his admiration for her life and work.

If God is pleased with this small and insignificant beginning, in time it could become a convent!

On November 5, 1849 Katharine Schoenberger joined the group. She was soon followed by Anne Marie Mueller, Elisabeth Meuser and Elisabeth Haas...

Thus was laid the foundation of a religious community in the "Little House" in Dernbach.

All our works, our words and thoughts must be prayer!

26

ON THE 1ST OF FEBRUARY, 1850 THE BISHOP APPROVED A RULE OF LIFE FOR THE YOUNG COMMUNITY. BEFORE THESE STATUTES COULD RECEIVE FINAL APPROVAL, A NAME FOR THE SOCIETY HAD TO BE FOUND.

Dear Bishop Blum, I request that you give our community the title "Poor Handmaids of Jesus Christ."

AFTER RECEIVING THE STATUTES FROM THE BISHOP, KATHERINE'S CONCERN WAS TO PUT THEM INTO PRACTICE RIGHT AWAY.

DURING THAT YEAR EIGHT ORPHAN CHILDREN WERE ADMITTED. THE "LITTLE HOUSE" HAD TO BE ENLARGED TO ACCOMMODATE THE INCREASING NUMBER OF MEMBERS AND ORPHANS.

A NEW WING WAS STARTED. KATHERINE AND HER COMPANIONS TOOK AN ACTIVE PART IN THE WORK FOR THE NEW WING, ESPECIALLY, IN THE BRICK-MAKING.

However, the community still longed to dedicate themselves to God through religious vows. On August 15, 1851 in the Parish Church of Wirges, Bishop Blum witnessed the fulfillment of their desire. The women consecrated themselves to God through the vows of obedience, poverty and celibacy.

A YEAR LATER KATHERINE TOOK THE RELIGIOUS NAME OF MARY.

THE SISTERS' LIFESTYLE CONTINUED TO BE ONE OF GREAT SIMPLICITY AND POVERTY. THEIR DIET CONSISTED OF A BOWL OF SOUP, SOME VEGETABLES AND A PIECE OF BLACK BREAD. WITH THIS THEY WERE SATISFIED. EVEN IN TIMES OF SUCH SHORTAGE, THEY DISTRIBUTED SOUP DAILY TO THE HUNGRY AND NEEDY.

God bless you, Mother Mary!

ONE DAY A REDEMPTORIST PRIEST VISITED THEM AND WAS AMAZED TO WITNESS SUCH POVERTY.

How long do you think you and your Sisters can keep up your strength with such little food?

You know, I have complete confidence that God, through this little bit of food, can sustain our strength.

You can't go on like this!

As soon as the convent is in the position to offer more, I will accept it as a sign from God.

Keep going as you are, Reverend Mother. You are on the right path.

LATER SHE SAID: "WE CERTAINLY FELT OUR POVERTY, BUT BECAUSE OF IT WE WERE GIVEN A HEAVENLY FORETASTE OF THE POVERTY OF RELIGIOUS LIFE IN WHICH WE POSSESS NOTHING AND YET HAVE EVERYTHING."

THE SISTERS CONTINUED TO WORK HARD, WERE LOVED AND RESPECTED IN THE AREA, AND AS A RESULT MANY YOUNG WOMEN WERE ATTRACTED TO THEM AND BECAME SISTERS.

MOTHER MARY WANTED TO ACCEPT ONLY THOSE WHO HAD A TRUE VOCATION.

"We always need prayerful sisters, even if we have thousands of them. But if we have sisters who are not prayerful or not loving.. even one is too many."

REQUESTS FOR THE SISTERS' CARE INCREASED MORE AND MORE AND GOD BLESSED THE COMMUNITY WITH NEW MEMBERS.

IN THE YEARS 1853-56 NINE NEW CONVENTS WERE OPENED. AS THE CONGREGATION GREW, THE SPACE OF THE MOTHERHOUSE ALSO NEEDED TO INCREASE.

FROM THE BEGINNING, THE SISTERS CARED FOR ORPHAN CHILDREN AND SAW THAT THEY ATTENDED SCHOOL.

THE VILLAGE AUTHORITIES, HOWEVER, DISLIKED THE IDEA OF SUCH CHILDREN ATTENDING THE VILLAGE SCHOOL.

The number of these children keeps increasing!

This costs even more money!

And who is going to pay?

We are!

This cannot go on!

THE MANY DIFFERENT BACKGROUNDS OF THESE CHILDREN OFTEN CAUSED PROBLEMS. SO THE AUTHORITIES THOUGHT THE CHILDREN WOULD BENEFIT IF EDUCATED IN THE CONVENT. FR. WITTAYER AND MR. SCHWARZ, A QUALIFIED TEACHER, WHO OFFERED HIS SERVICES FREE, CONDUCTED THE FIRST CLASSES. MOTHER MARY MADE EVERY EFFORT TO FIND SISTERS WHO COULD BE TRAINED AS TEACHERS.

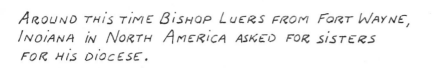

AROUND THIS TIME BISHOP LUERS FROM FORT WAYNE, INDIANA IN NORTH AMERICA ASKED FOR SISTERS FOR HIS DIOCESE.

ON JULY 30, 1868, MOTHER MARY TOOK EIGHT SISTERS AS FAR AS LE HAVRE FROM WHERE, A FORTNIGHT LATER, THEY SET SAIL FOR THE USA.

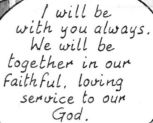

I will be with you always. We will be together in our faithful, loving service to our God.

ON AUGUST 28TH, THE EIGHT SISTERS ARRIVED SAFELY IN FORT WAYNE. THEIR TASK WAS TO TEACH THE CHILDREN IN THE GERMAN IMMIGRANT PARISHES.

AT THE BEGINNING THEY LIVED THERE, TOO, IN GREAT POVERTY.

BUT BEFORE LONG THIS SMALL SEED TOOK ROOT IN AMERICAN SOIL AND BECAME A GREAT TREE.

DESPITE HER DEEP DESIRE TO VISIT THE SISTERS IN THE U.S., THE FOUNDRESS WAS NEVER ABLE TO TRAVEL TO AMERICA. HER FREQUENT LETTERS AND HER DAILY PRAYERS CROSSED THE VAST OCEAN BETWEEN THEM.

TRAVELING ON FOOT, MOTHER MARY OFTEN VISITED ALL HER CONVENTS. THESE "VISITATIONS" WERE JUST AS IMPORTANT TO HER AND THROUGH THEM, SHE ENCOURAGED THE SISTERS IN LIVING OUT THEIR VOWS.

We are not here to be understood and loved, but to know and love God!

ONCE, AFTER SHE HAD SPOKEN TO A SISTER ABOUT SPIRITUAL MATTERS, SHE ASKED:

Do you understand that?

Yes, Mother, but I can't repeat it!

That is true! It is like the air; one feels it but one can't grasp it.

THE POOR HANDMAIDS OF JESUS CHRIST, AS ALL CONGREGATIONS OF THE TIME, SUFFERED MUCH DURING THE FOLLOWING YEARS: THE "KULTURKAMPF" OR THE ANTI-CATHOLIC LAWS OF 1872 HAD ALREADY FORCED THE CLOSING OF MANY CATHOLIC SCHOOLS AND EVENTUALLY LED TO THE SO CALLED "CONVENT-LAWS."

All religious orders and similar congregations of the Catholic church are disbanded by decree of the Prussian Monarchy. Convents of orders or congregations which exclusively dedicate themselves to health care can remain open. These however can at any time be closed by imperial decree. These "May Laws" were carried out seriously.

AT THE END OF JULY, 1875, THE SCHOOL AT MONTABAUR UNDERWENT A STATE INSPECTION.

This school must be closed in October of next year!

SIMILAR REPORTS FROM MANY OTHER CONVENTS REACHED THE MOTHERHOUSE. RELIGIOUS COMMUNITIES WERE THREATENED WITH ALMOST COMPLETE DISSOLUTION. HOW GOOD IT WAS, THAT AT THIS TIME, A PRIEST FROM LONDON ASKED FOR SISTERS TO HELP IN HIS PARISH.

THE NETHERLANDS, TOO, OFFERED THE SISTERS A NEW HOME.

In spite of these severe trials the congregation celebrated its Silver Jubilee in 1876. On this occasion the sisters gave their foundress a beautiful picture...

How do you like the painting, Mother?

It is very nice!... but the money would have been better spent, if you had shared it with the poor.

MOTHER MARY SECRETLY TRIED TO DISFIGURE HER LIKENESS.

During the years of the "Kulturkampf" Mother Mary Katherine's great concern was to protect the sisters against discouragement and anxiety. She wrote to them in 1878:

"My dear Sisters, even though the year 1878 lies dark and threatening before us, it is enough for us to know that nothing can happen to us outside of God's knowledge and wisdom. We must will only what God wills, as God wills it, and because God wills it."

Your unworthy

M. Maria

PHJC

After the German people suffered so much during the years of the "Kulturkampf", the government finally relented.

In 1880 it brought in a mitigating law which made things somewhat easier. In 1883 the sisters were again able to conduct kindergartens.

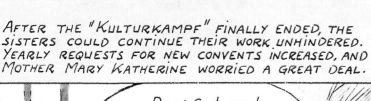
AFTER THE "KULTURKAMPF" FINALLY ENDED, THE SISTERS COULD CONTINUE THEIR WORK UNHINDERED. YEARLY REQUESTS FOR NEW CONVENTS INCREASED, AND MOTHER MARY KATHERINE WORRIED A GREAT DEAL.

Dear God, send our congregation only true vocations, only those you have called!

DESPITE INCREASING AGE AND POOR HEALTH, MOTHER MARY KATHERINE GAVE HERSELF NO REST, BUT CONTINUED TO MAKE STRENUOUS VISITATION JOURNEYS.

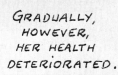
GRADUALLY, HOWEVER, HER HEALTH DETERIORATED.

I look on growing old as a special grace, because every day brings me closer to the Lord in his heavenly glory.

It is obvious that Mother Mary is looking forward to her death.

Did she not describe heaven as the biggest convent of the Poor Handmaids of Jesus Christ?

37

At the end of January 1898, Mother Mary Katherine did not feel well and was in great pain.

A few days later, however, she had a stroke and became unconscious. When she gained consciousness, she whispered,

Do not speak about my condition to anybody; I only need a rest.

Don't worry! I'm going to die!

All the Sisters wanted to see Mother Mary once more and receive her blessing.

Daughters, remain loving and prayerful. Continue as you are now and then you will be happy in eternity!

MOTHER MARY KATHERINE DIED FEBRUARY 2, 1898.
HER LIFE-WORK CONTINUES TO THIS DAY.
POOR HANDMAIDS OF JESUS CHRIST LIVE AND
WORK IN SIX COUNTRIES AND ON THREE CONTINENTS.
THE WORK BEGUN BY A YOUNG WOMAN IN AN OBSCURE
VILLAGE OF WEST GERMANY IS STILL BEING
CARRIED ON BY
MOTHER MARY
KATHERINE'S
SISTERS.